MARIE'S ELECTRIC ADVENTURE

"Goodnight Marie," Marie's
mom says as she turns
to leave the bedroom.
"Wait, don't forget to turn
on the nightlight!"

In the glow of the nightlight, Marie clutches her stuffed penguin and listens to the thunder. Einstein snores softly under her bed.

BOOM! FLASH!
Einstein lets out
a yip, and the
nightlight goes out.

"Mom!" Marie shouts.
Mom pops her head
into the room.
"Everything is OK, Marie.
The power just went out.
Try to go back to sleep."

Marie tosses and
turns in her bed.
There is no way she
can sleep without
her nightlight!
Marie sighs and
looks at Einstein.

Einstein says, "Well, I guess we have to do something. Maybe it has to do with the nuclear plant I heard the squirrels talking about. Let's go check it out."

"No, Einstein! It's too scary outside," Marie says. Einstein grabs the flashlight from under the bed and says, "Don't worry, we can go together."

Bravely, Marie follows Einstein outside and looks around her yard. "Power ... Power ... Where does the power come from?" Marie asks.

WELCOME

Einstein runs across the yard. "Power comes from power lines. Maybe we can follow them back to the nuclear plant."

Marie and Einstein follow
the power lines into the woods.
Marie trips.
"Ouch!" She glances behind
her and can't see her house
through the darkness.
"Where are we? Maybe
we should go back."

Einstein starts to say something
when an owl hoots.
"WHOOOOOO."
Einstein exclaims, "Oh! A big bird.
Let's go get the big bird!"
and runs after the owl.

Marie sprints after Einstein
straight into a fence.
"Ooof!" From the ground, Marie
looks way ... way ... way up.

Marie sees a huge tower
burping what looks like
smoke into the night sky.

A deep voice asks, "Who are *you* ?"
Marie screams and jumps up.
The tall tree next to the
fence blinks and looks
at Einstein and Marie.
Einstein asks, "Who are
you?"

The tree says,
"My name is Adam.
I live by the nuclear
power plant."
Marie bursts out, "I need to turn
my nightlight back on, and your
power plant is broken!"

A gust of wind blows the storm cloud away. Adam says, "Actually, the storm blew over a power line. There is nothing wrong with the nuclear plant. It runs all the time no matter what the weather is like."

Seeing Marie's puzzled look,
Adam explains how the
nuclear plant works.
"We slam atoms together."
Adam claps his branches
together like giant hands.
"And then the atoms break apart."
Adam spreads his leaves out like fingers.

"The atoms give off energy that turns water into steam. The steam turns a giant fan that spins a machine that makes electricity."

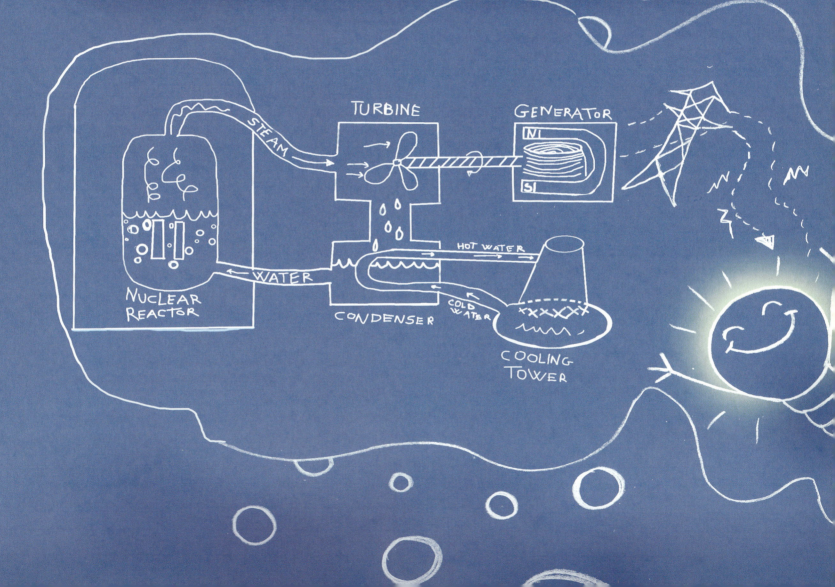

Marie worries about the smoke coming out of the tower. "What about that big tower?"

Adam says, "I know it looks like smoke,
but what is coming out of the cooling
tower is actually just gassy water."
Einstein toots.
"No, Einstein-not that kind of gas.
It is like the steam you see when
you are cooking."
Einstein wags his tail.

Adam promises, "As soon as the power lines are connected again, you can go back to using power for everything you need, including your nightlight. It's getting late," yawns Adam. "Do you both know how to get home?" Einstein nods and wags his tail.

"Good night." Adam waves his leafy branches as they turn and walk away. Marie and Einstein splash their way back to the house.

As they leave the woods, the street
lights turn on all at once.
"Look, the lights came back on!"
exclaims Marie.

"See? Everything is as good as new. There's nothing to be afraid of in the dark," says Einstein.

"Or at the nuclear power plant,"
Marie adds.
She looks at Einstein, "Just because
something seems scary doesn't mean
it really is."

Back in bed, Marie snuggles
with her stuffed penguin.
"Einstein, I don't think
I need a nightlight tonight.
I'm not scared anymore."

We hope you enjoyed Marie and Einstein's story about nuclear energy! Electricity is interesting and safe as long as you follow a few rules:

1. Do not touch electrical outlets or cords without an adult's permission.
2. Keep electrical devices away from water.
3. Stay away from power lines (especially if they are on the ground) and electrical equipment. Electricity can flow to other nearby objects—keep your distance!

And remember, never go outside at night alone!

Glossary

Atoms: the tiny building blocks of matter

Burst: to talk excitedly

Clutch: to hold

Connect: to become joined

Cooling Tower: a structure that reduces water temperature at a power plant. Hot water flows down within the tower like a waterfall. This forces air up, which cools the water, and some of the water evaporates out of the top.

Electric: (1) uses electricity or (2) exciting

Electricity: the movement of electrons through a conductor (such as a wire or power line)

Exclaim: to say something suddenly and loudly

Glance: a quick look

Gust: a sudden wind

Nuclear: science and technology based on the nucleus (center of an atom)

Power Lines: cables carrying electrical power

Power: energy that can be used to operate a machine

Puzzled: confused or not understanding

Sprint: to run at top speed

Steam: vapor produced when water is boiled

Yip: to bark quickly

Authors' Note

The characters in this story are named after important scientists in nuclear science history. Marie Curie, along with her husband Pierre Curie and colleague Henri Becquerel, was awarded a Nobel Prize in Physics for her discovery of the radioactive elements polonium and radium. Marie went on to receive a Nobel Prize in Chemistry for her continued investigation of these elements.

Albert Einstein was a scientist (not a dog) and made many significant contributions to nuclear science. His theory of special relativity shows a direct relationship between energy and mass conversion. This is more commonly known as $E=mc^2$.

The name Adam is symbolic for atom. Atoms are the tiny building blocks of matter. Nuclear energy is the heat released by splitting atoms (this process is called fission). The heat increases the temperature of water and turns it into steam. The steam rotates a turbine (similar to a fan), which is on the same shaft as a generator. When the generator rotates, it creates a magnetic field to charge wires and produce electricity.

As of 2016, nuclear energy provides more than 60% of the carbon-free electricity in the United States! Other types of power plants, like coal- and natural gas-fired plants, use similar principles to create electricity from a heat source. The main difference is the method by which they produce heat. By splitting atoms instead of burning a fuel source (such as coal or natural gas), nuclear power plants do not release carbon into the environment when they produce electricity.

For more information about nuclear energy, check out the following resource:

http://naygn.org/committees/public-information/public-information-library/

Project Funded by North American Young Generation in Nuclear
Project Organized and Written by the Following Members of the Duke Energy Chapter of North American Young Generation in Nuclear

Adam Reichenbach
Alyse Scurlock
Amanda Lang
Andy Kalchik
Anne McGovern
Ashley Marlowe
Christine Johnsen

Glen Lawson
Jennifer Taylor
Kyle Hemker
Matthew Bradfield
Meaghann Zeiner
Seth Weir

Published by
North American Young Generation in Nuclear (NAYGN)
P.O. Box 32642, Charlotte, NC 28232 USA

Illustrated by
Kezia Terracciano
www.keziat.net

Manufactured in the United States.

978-0-578-19424-0